CONTENTS

You will need a performing licence to stage this musical / nativity
See back of book for details
Removable Label

CURRICULUM LINKS

Song 1 The Big Star

Personal, social and emotional development:
Talk about how the big star might have felt when he realised he could no longer shine. How can we help our friends when they feel they can't do something?

Physical development: Pretend to be the big star and add actions to match the lyrics as you sing this song.

Song 2 A Baby Is Going To Be Born

Knowledge and understanding of the world:
Where are babies usually born? What other reasons might you visit a hospital? Have any of the children been to hospital? Can they talk about their experience?

Creative development: Turn your role play area into a doctor's surgery or hospital and allow the children to explore and freely express their ideas.

Song 3 Too Dark!

Knowledge and understanding of the world:
Talk about light and dark. When is it light and when is it dark? What things in the sky, other than stars, make light? What sorts of things do we use to light our homes, streets, cars, etc?

Creative development: Make some lanterns using differently coloured tissue paper and black card. Cut shapes in the card and stick the tissue paper onto the back of this, so it shows through the holes. Wrap the card around and secure with sticky tape, making a lantern shape. Add a strip of card at the top for the handle. Carefully use candles or shine a torch to make the lantern shine.

Communication, language and literacy:
There are lots of action words in this song describing how the shepherds travelled on their journey to Bethlehem. Can the children think of any more that would fit into the verses?

Ask the children to make up a story about their journey to school/ nursery, using as many descriptive words as they can.

Song 4 Hey Star

Knowledge and understanding of the world:

What would you find in a desert? Is it hot or cold? Is there much water? Would there have been any shops there when Jesus was born?

Can the children suggest things we use nowadays to find our way (eg maps, road signs, sat navs!)? Can they imagine what it would have been like to using stars to guide the way?

Song 5 Shine Star, Shine

Creative development: Make pictures or collages of the night-time sky. These could be included in the scenery for the play.

Gather together a selection of percussion instruments, both tuned and untuned. Let the children explore the sounds each makes, then ask them to choose some that would best symbolize a star shining. Remember that there are no wrong or right sounds for this; the children should be free to express their own ideas. You could choose some of the sounds and rhythms played by the children to accompany the song in the final performance.

Song 6 Far Below

Knowledge and understanding of the world:

Talk about the nativity story and why the baby was so special.

Personal, social and emotional development:

In the story, the star started to shine when it saw the baby Jesus. Can the children remember why this was? What sorts of things make the children feel happy, loved, sad, excited, lonely? Talk about being thoughtful and caring towards one another and why this is important.

Song 7 Hallelujah!

Knowledge and understanding of the world:

At Christmas we celebrate the birth of Jesus. Talk about the sorts of things we do to celebrate and some of the reasons behind these traditions.

What do we celebrate at other times of the year?

CHARACTER LIST

Narrator	Can be read by an adult/older child, or split between a group of pupils.
Stars	Have as many of these as you like. There are short speaking lines for up to ten and a few unison lines for all. There is also an opportunity for some to read a poem/story, tell jokes, dance and even sing a short song when they are trying to make the big star shine.
Big Star	The title role, but only a few very simple lines to say. Some acting ability would be useful, with lots of huffing and puffing needed during the first song!
Angel	One important line to deliver to the shepherds.
Shepherds	There should be a group of shepherds, all of whom will need to perform the actions in the lyrics of song 3. There are short lines for three and one simple unison line.
Sheep	If you have enough of a cast, you may want to incorporate some sheep. Otherwise these can simply be painted into the scenery or held as soft toys.
Kings	You'll need three kings. They have one line each and one to say in unison, and you can incorporate actions for them throughout song 4, if you wish.
Camels	Again, if you have the children available, it would be fun to cast some in these roles.
Mary	A non-speaking role. She'll need to sit in the stable as the big star looks down.
Joseph	Joins Mary in the stable for the nativity scene. Again, no lines to learn.
Baby Jesus	To lie in the manger – we think a doll works best!

STAGING

This really can be as simple or elaborate as you choose. The stable can be set slightly to one side leaving space around for the different journeys and scenes to take place. Also, have the choir/cast on risers/steps at the back ready to step forward when it's their turn to shine.

Script & Song Lyrics

NARRATOR Once upon a time there was a star who stopped shining. This star had been the biggest, brightest star in the whole sky, but one night, when he tried to sparkle, nothing happened. He tried and tried and he tried again, but the big star could not shine.

Song 1. THE BIG STAR **CD Track 1/8**

1. The big star tried with all his might,
He huffed and puffed into the night,
But though he was big, whatever he did,
He could not shine.

2. The big star puffed out his chest,
He really did try his best,
But though he was big, whatever he did,
He could not shine.

3. The big star jumped up and down,
He clapped his hands and turned around,
But though he was big, whatever he did,
He could not shine.

4. The big star tried with all his might,
He huffed and puffed into the night,
But though he was big, whatever he did,
He could not shine,
Could not shine.

NARRATOR The next night, the other stars came to see him. They were very excited because they had some important news.

STAR 1 A baby is going to be born.

STAR 2 In Bethlehem, in a stable.

STAR 3 He will be the Son of God.

STAR 4 His name will be Jesus.

Song 2. A BABY IS GOING TO BE BORN **CD Track 2/9**

1. A baby is going to be born,
A baby is going to be born.
Tonight, tonight in the bright starlight,
A baby is going to be born.

2. A stable is where he will be,
A stable is where he will be.
Tonight, tonight in the bright starlight,
A stable is where he will be.

3 The angels will sing in the sky,
The angels will sing in the sky.
Tonight, tonight in the bright starlight,
The angels will sing in the sky.

4 *Repeat verse 1*

NARRATOR The other stars had more news for the big star.

STAR 5 You have to shine brightly.

STAR 6 Very, very brightly!

STAR 7 To show people the way to the stable.

NARRATOR The big star looked at the other stars.

BIG STAR But I can't shine.

STARS Yes you can!

BIG STAR No I can't!

STARS Yes you can. Shine star, shine!

NARRATOR The big star tried and tried and tried, but he could not shine.

That night on the hills above Bethlehem, some shepherds were looking after their sheep. Suddenly an angel appeared in the sky. The angel spoke to the shepherds.

ANGEL You must go to Bethlehem. The baby Jesus has been born in a stable.

NARRATOR The shepherds were amazed to see the angel. They were very excited because they knew that the baby must be very special.

SHEPHERD 1 Isn't this exciting?

SHEPHERD 2 Let's go quickly.

SHEPHERD 3 Yes, let's go and see the baby!

NARRATOR In great excitement, the shepherds started to walk over the hills towards Bethlehem. It was hard to hurry because it was very, very dark.

Song 3. TOO DARK! **CD Track 3/10**

1 We're going to Bethlehem in the dark,
In the dark, in the dark,
We're going to Bethlehem in the dark
And it's too dark to see.

2 We're hurrying, hurrying in the dark,
In the dark, in the dark,
We're hurrying, hurrying in the dark
And it's too dark to see.

3 We're tripping up, tripping up in the dark,
In the dark, in the dark,
We're tripping up, tripping up in the dark
And it's too dark to see.

4 We're stumbling, stumbling in the dark,
In the dark, in the dark,
We're stumbling, stumbling in the dark
And it's too dark to see.

5 *Repeat verse 1*

NARRATOR Way up above, high in the sky, the smaller stars watched the shepherds as they stumbled in the dark. They knew that the big star could help and they called loudly to him.

STARS Shine star, shine!

NARRATOR The big star tried and tried and tried, but he could not shine.

Far away in the east, three wise kings were travelling to Bethlehem to see the baby Jesus. They were sure that there had been a big, bright star in the sky, but now it was nowhere to be seen.

KING 1 Where is that star?

KING 2 I don't know!

KING 3 It was here last night!

Song 4. HEY STAR **CD Track 4/11**

1 Riding in the desert, looking for a star,
We've got a long way to go,
We really don't know where we are,
This journey is so slow.

CHORUS *Hey star,*
Why don't you show us the way to go?

2 On and on and into the night,
Riding to and fro,
All we want is a bit of light,
So we would like to know,

CHORUS

3 *Instrumental*

CHORUS

4 Riding in the desert, looking for a star,
We've got a long way to go,
We really don't know where we are,
This journey is so slow.

CHORUS

NARRATOR Way up above in the sky, the other stars watched the kings as they rode on their camels. They called loudly again to the big star.

STARS Shine star, shine!

NARRATOR The big star tried and tried and tried but he could not shine. The other stars didn't know what to do.

STAR 8 You have to shine, big star!

STAR 9 Please try harder!

STAR 10 It's really important!

NARRATOR The big star tried again. He tried and tried and tried and tried, but still he could not shine. The other stars also tried everything they could.

They read him a story… they told him a joke… they did a funny dance… and they sang him a song.

Song 5. SHINE STAR, SHINE **CD Track 5/12**

1 You are a beautiful star, gliding high,
Floating in the dark, in the sky.
So shine star, shine,
Shine star, shine,
All you have to do is shine.

2 You are the biggest star and you have a job to do.
Can you make a start 'cos we depend on you?
So shine star, shine,
Shine star, shine,
All you have to do is shine.

3 *Repeat verse 1*

NARRATOR The stars tried and tried but nothing worked; the big star still could not shine. The other stars thought for a while, then suddenly had an idea. They led the big star through the sky to the stable in Bethlehem. Looking into the stable, the big star saw Mary and Joseph and a beautiful baby. As he watched, he could feel that the baby loved him; that the baby Jesus loved all the stars and all the angels and all the people in the whole world.

The big star began to shine. He shone and shone, brighter and brighter and floated up into the sky above the stable. His light could be seen for miles and miles. The stable glowed in the starlight and the baby Jesus slept peacefully in the manger.

Song 6. FAR BELOW **CD Track 6/13**

1 Down through the night the starlight came
And made the stable glow,
And there in a manger Jesus lay,
Far below, far below.

2 All through the night the star shone bright,
It showed us where to go,
And there in a manger Jesus lay,
Far below, far below.

3 *Instrumental*

4 Down through the night the starlight came
And made the stable glow,
And there in a manger Jesus lay,
Far below, far below.
Far below, far below.

NARRATOR The light from the big star spread over the hills and out across the land. The shepherds found their way to the stable.

SHEPHERDS What a beautiful baby!

NARRATOR Then the kings arrived and gave the baby Jesus some lovely gifts.

KINGS We worship you, great king!

NARRATOR And so the big star shone brightly in the sky. He shone his light down over the stable, where a very special baby lay, on that very special night.

Song 7. HALLELUJAH! **CD Track 7/14**

1 Come to the stable, follow me,
Come to the stable, follow me,
There is a newborn king to see,
Hallelujah, hallelujah!

2 He brings His love for everyone,
He brings His love for everyone,
He is Jesus, God's own son,
Hallelujah, hallelujah!

3 And His love will make us shine,
And His love will make us shine,
Shine until the end of time,
Hallelujah, hallelujah!

4 *Repeat verse 1*

The Big Star

Words and Music by
Niki Davies

CCLI Song No. 5510267

To Coda
1. 2.
Dm7
G7
C
Dm/C
Cmaj7
Dm/C
C
Dm/C
could not shine.
could not shine.
could not
3.
Dm7
G7
C
G7
C
A7
Dm7
G7
C
A7
2. The shine.
3. The
D.S. al Coda
Dm7
G7
C
E7
A7
Dm7
G7
C
G7
4. The
CODA
C
A7
Dm7
G7
C
G7
C
shine, could not shine.

A Baby Is Going To Be Born

Words and Music by
Niki Davies

1. 2. 3.
Bm7 E7 A F♯m7 Bm7 E7
ba - by is going to be born.
sta - ble is where he will be.
an - gels will sing in the sky.

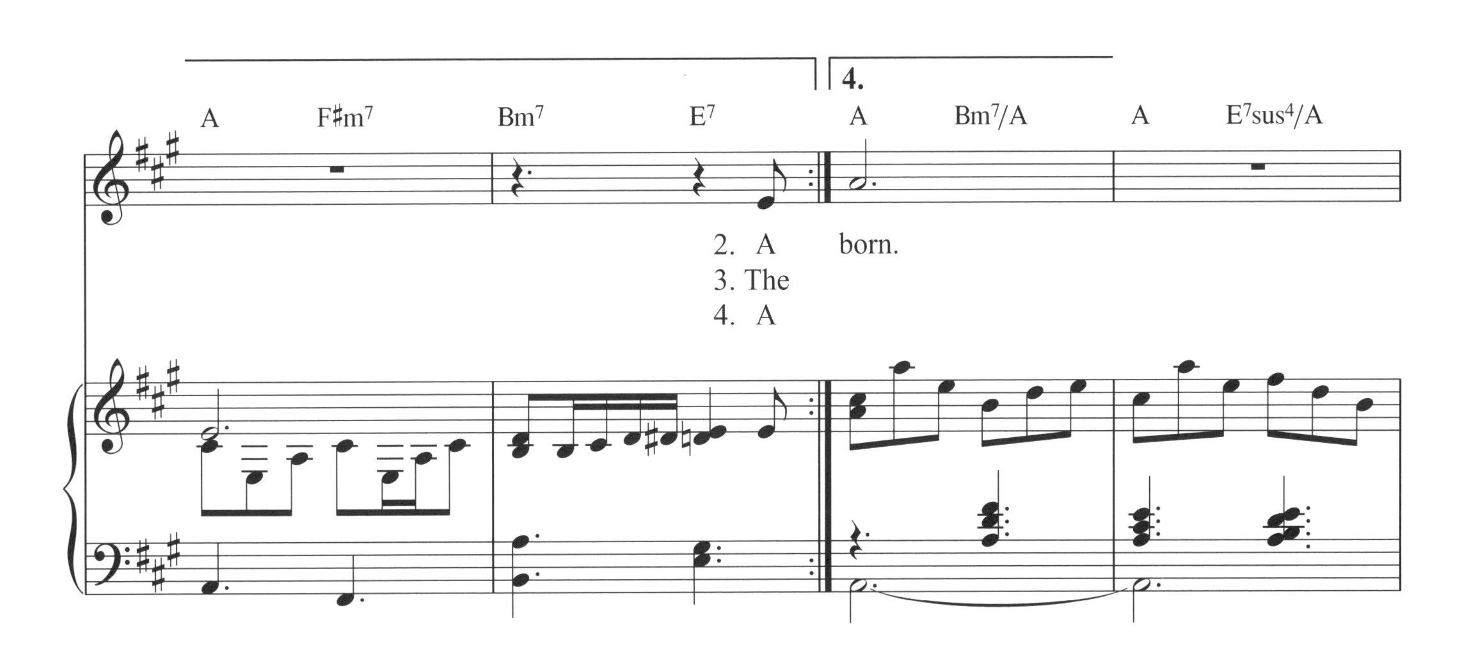
4.
A F♯m7 Bm7 E7 A Bm7/A A E7sus4/A
2. A born.
3. The
4. A

rit.
A Bm7/A A E7sus4/A A Bm/A A D/A A

Too Dark!

Words and Music by
Niki Davies

Moderately ♩ = 152

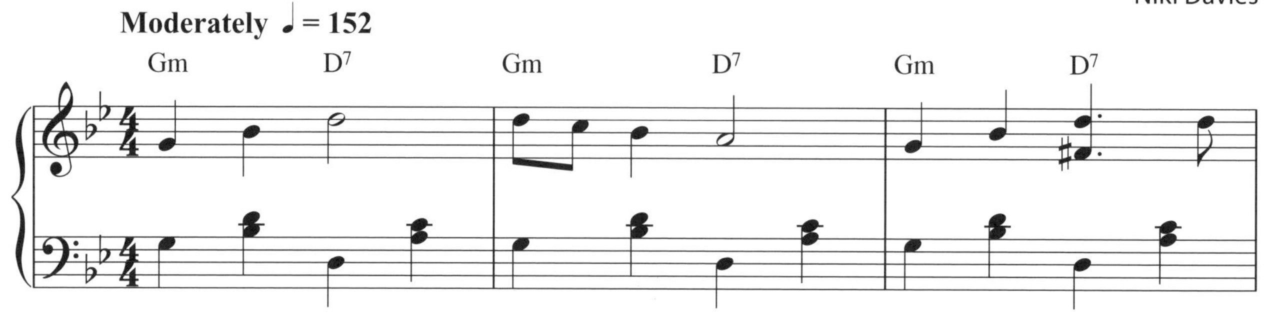

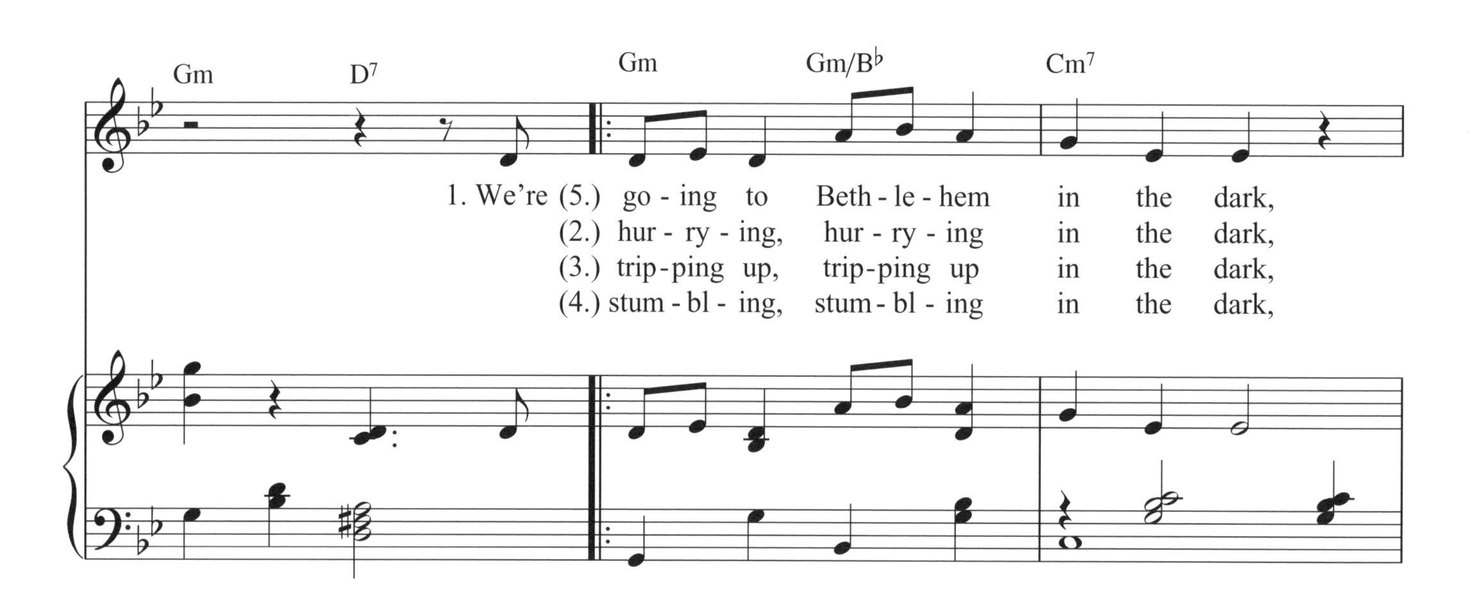

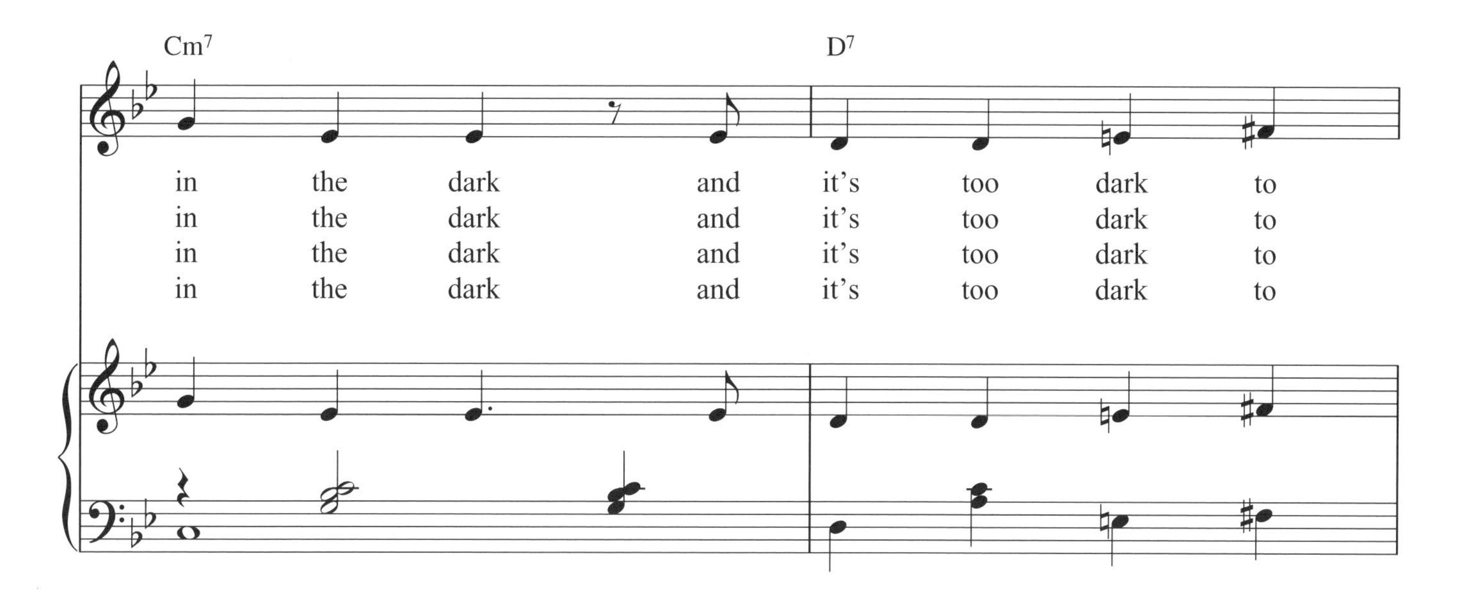
Cm7
D7
in the dark and it's too dark to
in the dark and it's too dark to
in the dark and it's too dark to
in the dark and it's too dark to

1 – 4.
5.
Gm
D7
Gm
D7
Gm
D7
see.
see.
see.
see.
2. We're
3. We're
4. We're
5. We're
see.

Gm
D7
Gm
D7
Gm
3

Hey Star

Words and Music by
Niki Davies

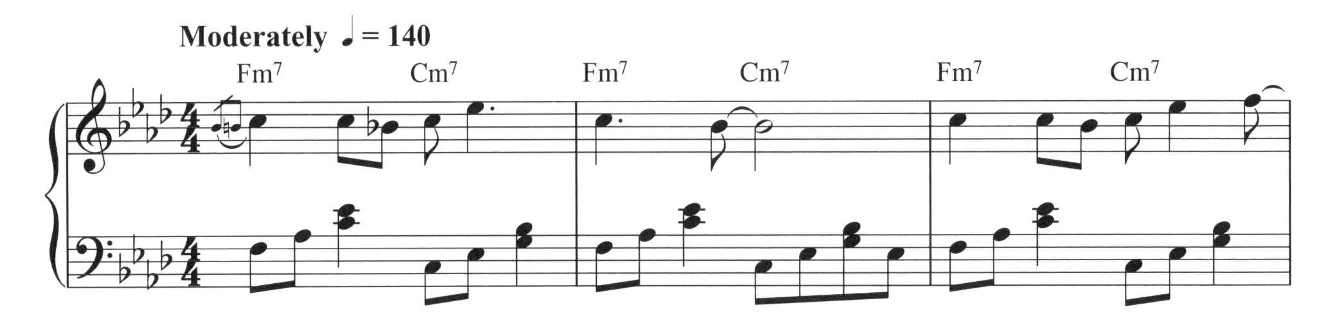

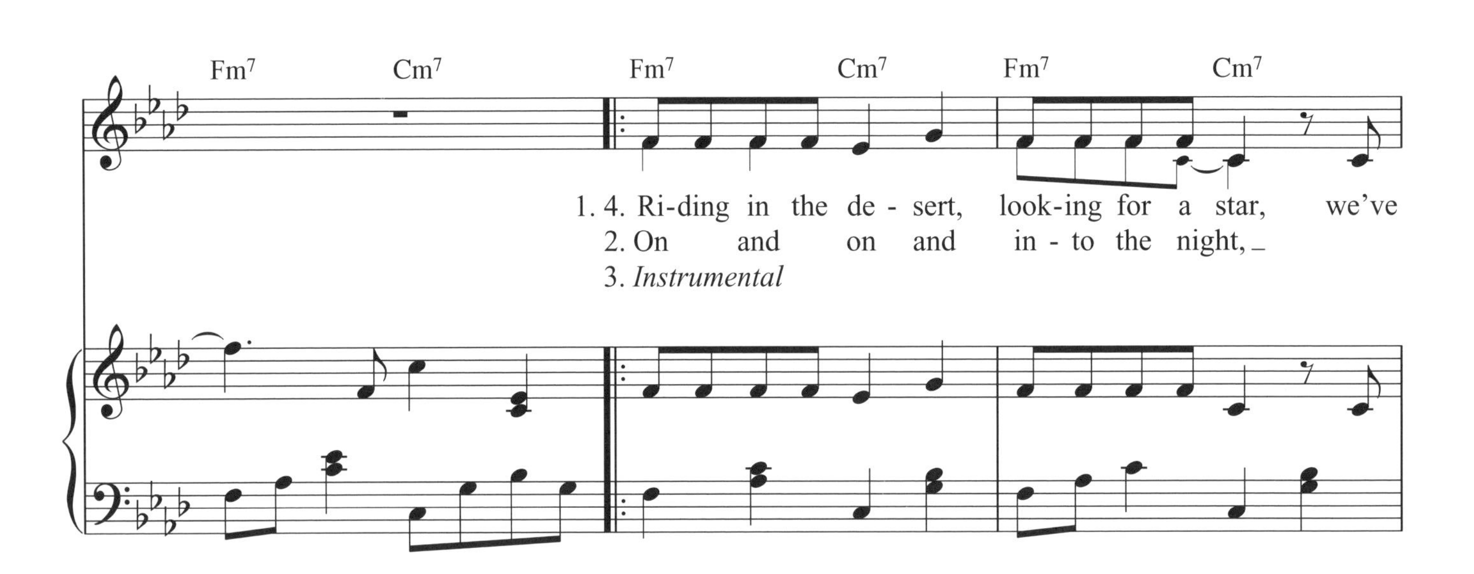

Fm7
Cm7
Fm7
Cm7
Fm7
where we are, this jour - ney is so slow.
bit of light, so we would like to know,
Hey

1. 2. 3.
B♭m7
E♭13
A♭
Fm7
B♭m7
Caug C
star, why don't you show us the way to go?

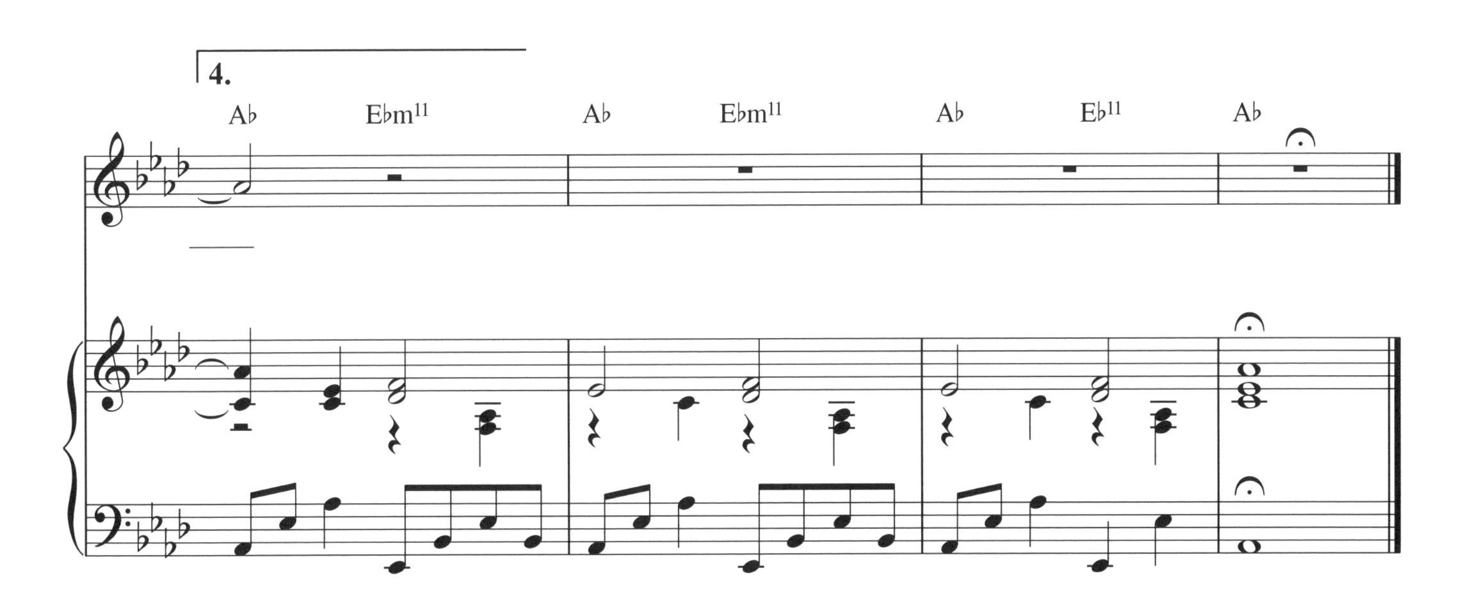
4.
A♭
E♭m11
A♭
E♭m11
A♭
E♭11
A♭

Shine Star, Shine

Words and Music by
Niki Davies

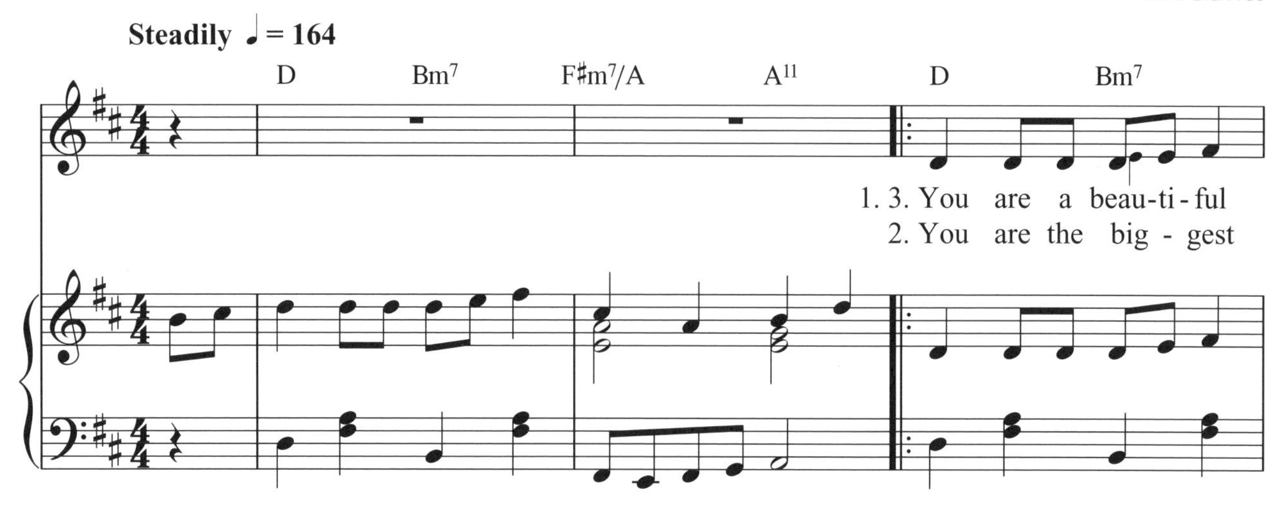

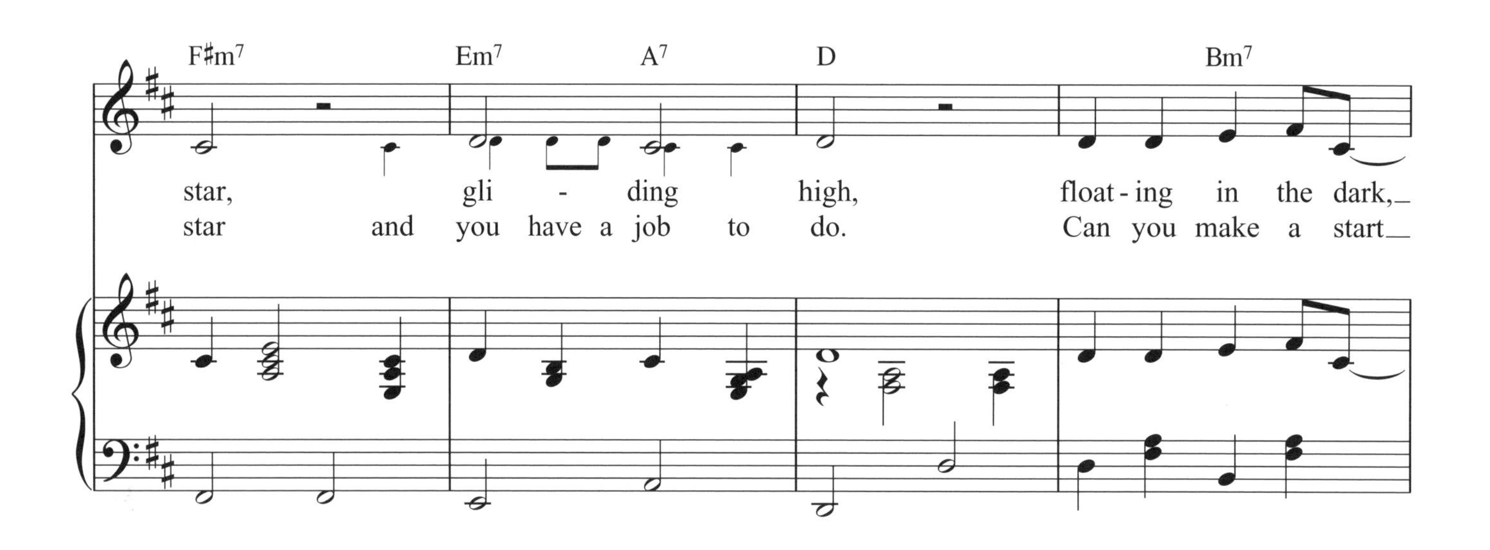

Em7 A7 F♯7 Em7 A7
shine star, shine, all you have_ to do__ is
1. 2.
D Em7/D Dmaj7 Em7/D Dmaj7 G/D A7sus4 A7
shine.
3.
D Em7/D Dmaj7 Em7/D D Em7/D Dmaj7 Em7/D
shine.__
rit.
D Em7/D Dmaj7 Em7/D Dmaj7 Em7/D Dmaj7 Em7/D D

Far Below

Words and Music by
Niki Davies

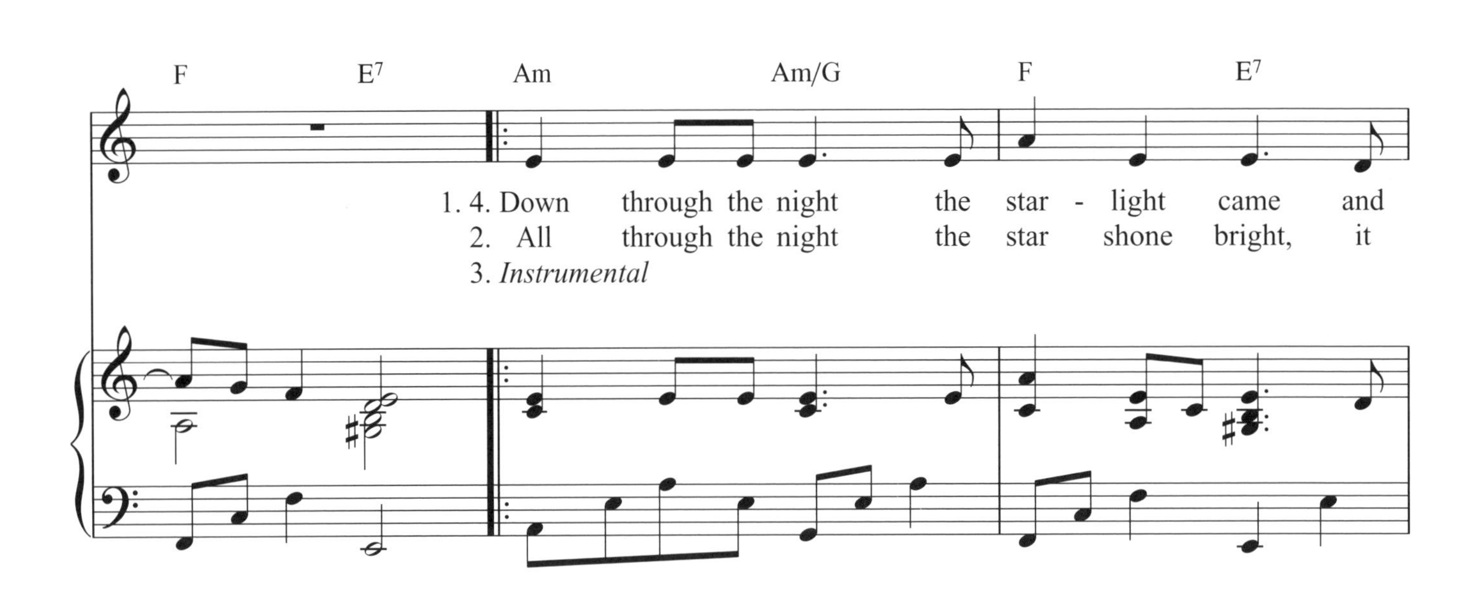

1. 2. 3.
Dm
Dm/C
G7/B
G7
C
Dm7
E7
- low,
far be - low.
- low,
far be - low.

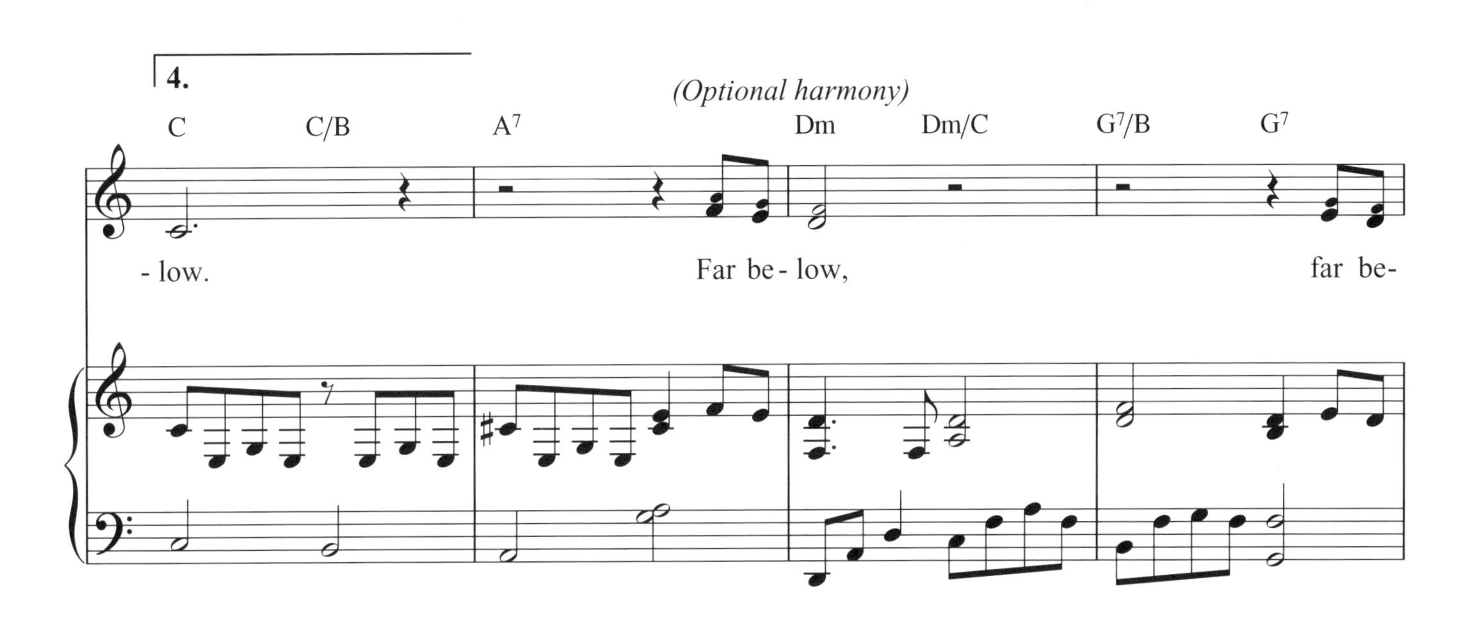
4.
(Optional harmony)
C
C/B
A7
Dm
Dm/C
G7/B
G7
- low.
Far be - low,
far be-

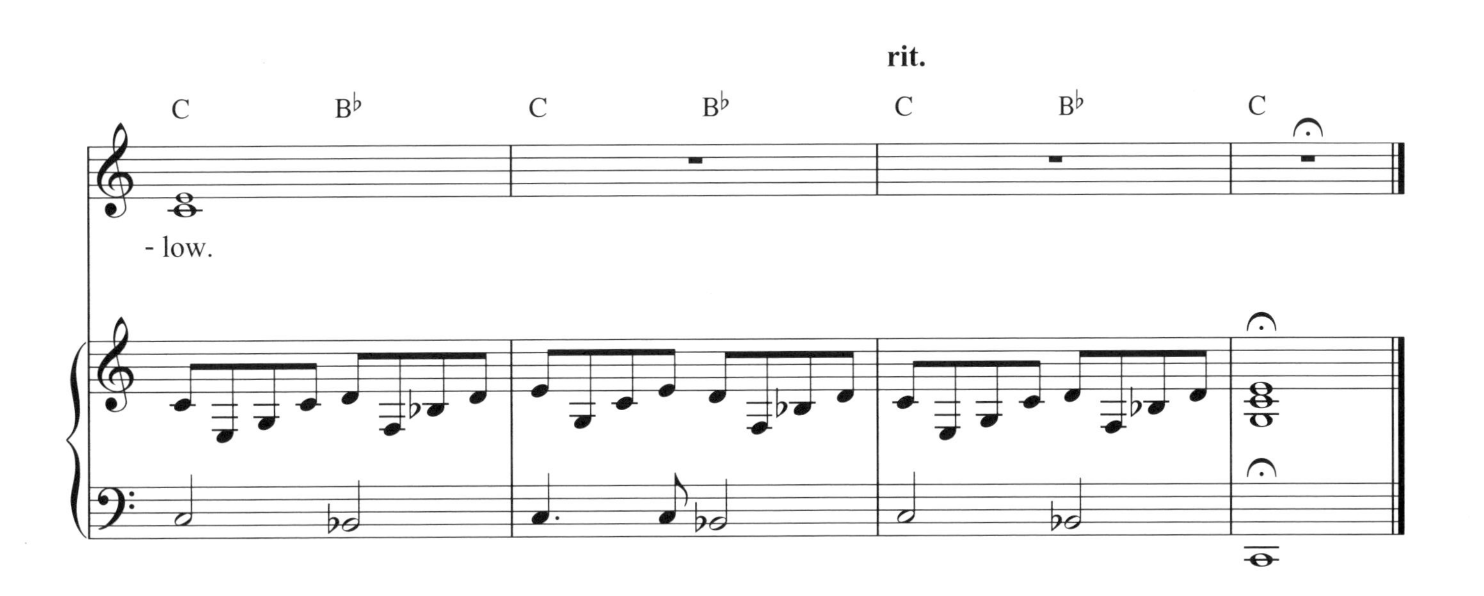
rit.
C
B♭
C
B♭
C
B♭
C
- low.

Hallelujah!

Words and Music by
Niki Davies

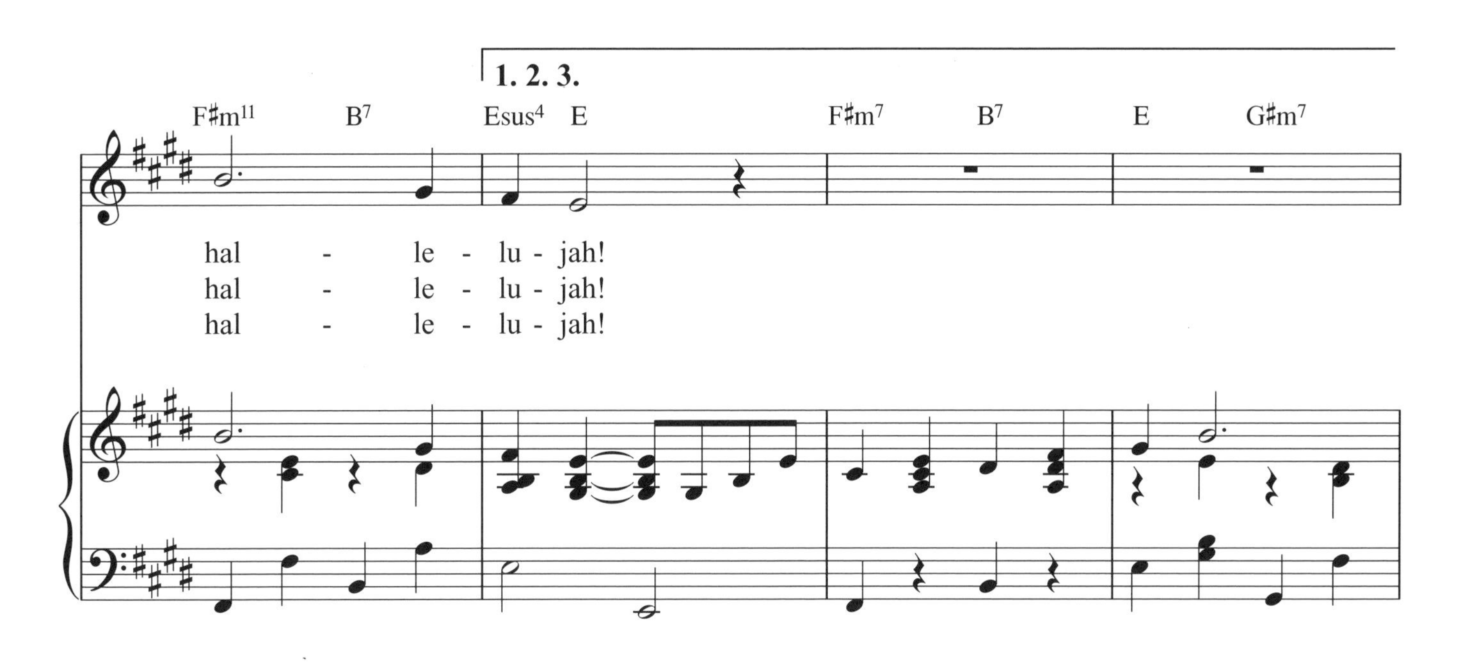
1. 2. 3.
F♯m11 B7 Esus4 E F♯m7 B7 E G♯m7
hal - le - lu - jah!
hal - le - lu - jah!
hal - le - lu - jah!

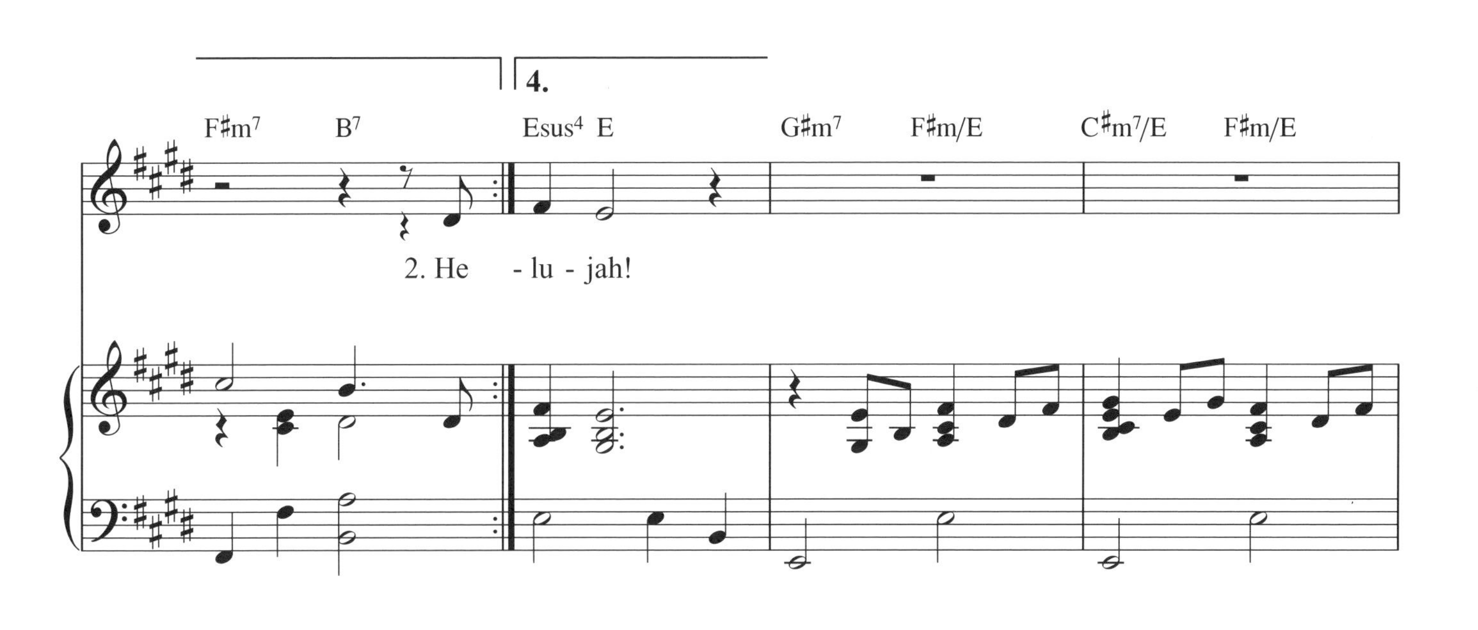
4.
F♯m7 B7 Esus4 E G♯m7 F♯m/E C♯m7/E F♯m/E
2. He - lu - jah!

G♯m/E F♯m7/E E

LICENCE APPLICATION FORM

(Shine Star, Shine)

If you perform **Shine Star, Shine** to an audience other than children and staff you will need to photocopy and complete this form and return it by post or fax to Out of the Ark Music in order to apply for a licence. If anticipated audience sizes are very small or if special circumstances apply please contact Out of the Ark Music.

The licence will permit the holder to:

- Perform *Shine Star, Shine* on the dates applied for.
- Reproduce the lyrics to the songs on printed paper, such as for programmes, and to make transparencies for overhead projection. The following credit should be included: *'Reproduced by kind permission © Out of the Ark Ltd'.*
- Photocopy the script for learning purposes. Copies must be destroyed after the performance.
- Make no more than two copies of the music, to be used by participating musicians on the performance dates.

If the performance is to be recorded please contact Out of the Ark Music.

We wish to apply for a licence to perform *Shine Star, Shine* by Niki Davies

Customer number (if known): ....

Name of school / organisation: ....

Name of organiser / producer: ....

Date(s) of performance(s): ....

Invoice address: ....

....

Post code: .... **Country:** ....

Telephone number: ....

Number of performances (excl. dress rehearsal)	**Performances without admission charges**	**Performances with admission charges**
1	☐ **£11.75*** [€17.50]	☐ **£18.80** [€28.00]
2 or more	☐ **£18.80** [€28.00]	☐ **£23.50** [€35.00]

Tick one of the boxes above.

☐ Tick here to receive licensing information for any audio or video recording of a performance.

Tick one of the four payment options below: (Invoices will be sent with all licences)

☐ Please bill my school/nursery at the above address (UK schools/nurseries only)

☐ I enclose a cheque (Pounds Sterling) for £ .... payable to Out of the Ark Music

☐ I enclose a cheque (Euro) for € .... payable to Out of the Ark Music

☐ Please charge the following card: (Visa [not Electron], MasterCard, Maestro & American Express accepted)

Card No ....

Start Date _ _ / _ _ (MM/YY) Expiry Date _ _ / _ _ (MM/YY) 3 digit security code: _ _ _ (last 3 digits on signature strip)

Address: Out of the Ark Music
Sefton House
2 Molesey Road
Hersham
Surrey KT12 4RQ
United Kingdom

Phone: +44 (0)1932 232250
Fax: +44 (0)1932 703010
Email: info@outoftheark.com

*The licence fees shown on this form are for 2009-2010 and include VAT at 17.5%. Prices may be subject to revision. Customers outside the EU will NOT be charged VAT.